What Would

1,001 Anytime Questions

It Be

for Anysize Answers

Like...?

Chris Cavert & Friends

Published by:

Wood & Barnes Publishing
2717 NW 50th
Oklahoma City, OK 73112
(405) 942-6812

1st Edition © 2006, Chris Cavert

Printed in the United States of America
Oklahoma City, Oklahoma
ISBN # 1-885473-77-X

Cover art by Blue Designs
Copyediting and design by Ramona Cunningham

To order copies of this book, please call:
Jean Barnes Books
800-678-0621

Acknowledgements

I want to thank all my young friends who contributed to this book. I appreciate the time you gave me and the fun conversations we had along the way.

Allison, Andrew, Barrett, Chris, Clayton, Colleen, Craig, Elizabeth, Hilary, Hunter, James, Jennifer, Jenny, Jonathan, Josh, Kathryn, Katie, Kenny, Lauren, Liz, Mary Carol, Molly, Rachael, Stefanie, Steven, Taylor, Tori, Warren, & Whitney.

A special thanks to my best friend and traveling companion, Susana Acosta. We filled a lot of miles together wondering "what would it be like...?"

Another big thanks goes to Michael and Brian Wood. I sure do appreciate all the great questions. I have enjoyed sharing them with my groups.

To Mom - Your love and spirit get me where I'm going. Thank you so much.

What would it be like...

- to wear pajamas all day?

- to read minds?

- to be caught shoplifting?

Introduction

What would it be like to have a whole bunch of questions that started with, "What would it be like...?" You're not sure? Well, here is your chance to find out."

These were the first few sentences in the introduction of the "What would it be like..." section in the revised and expanded edition of Games (& other stuff) for Group, Book 1, published in 1999. From this launching pad we have collected over 1000 of these "starters" to help initiate group discussions and conversations. The list that follows can be integrated into group sessions, transition times, etc. Anytime really. I hope you have as much fun with them as we do.

The following questions are presented in closed format. This means they can be answered with one word (usually a feeling word in this case). It is your choice as a facilitator to expand on the questions if you think the individual/group is ready to do so and you have the time. Sometimes it is better to let one-word answers be enough. This can build trust for future discussions.

If you would like to expand on the questions, here's the idea: "What would it be like to move to a new state?" Answers could vary from "scary" to "great, it would get me out of here!" Expanding on the responses is also wide open. "What sorts of things would be scary?" "Why do you want to get out of here?" Then expand upon those answers. You get the idea.

I have presented these questions a couple of ways. I've just opened the book and randomly asked questions. This makes the atmosphere relaxed and non-threatening. Other times I planned ahead and picked questions that related to a certain group discussion that I wanted to have. Both ways have worked well.

Be careful not to spend too much time with one person. I always allow the option to pass or choose a new question. (I usually don't allow more than one chance to pick another question - time problems). If the question seems to cause reactions with others, open the question up to the group. (I usually set up guidelines to prevent others from answering someone else's question or blurting out an answer.) Use your time evenly among the group members to keep the interest going.

Don't forget to take a turn yourself. It is a good way to become part of the group. Have fun with the questions so you'll leave them wanting more!

Chris Cavert

- to be respected?

- to ride in an open-air biplane?

- to receive a surprise birthday party?

- to always be last?

- to catch a fish with your bare hands?

- to conduct an orchestra?

- to wear pajamas all day?

- to read minds?

- to be caught shoplifting?

- if part of your family lived in another country?

- to go on a walk with a two-year-old?

- if you couldn't feel anything?

- to live without cell phones?

- to be at the bottom of the food chain?

- to find the city of Atlantis?

- to attend church every day?

What would it be like. . . ?. . .?. . .?

- if the American Melting Pot was "done"?

- to live on a house boat?

- to catch the bouquet?

- if the world was black and white?

- to liberate a suppressed people?

- to be known as a tattletale?

- to own McDonalds®?

- to get a tattoo?

- if your signature was worth money?

- to design your own amusement park?

- if there was no competition?

- to be unable to control your emotions?

- to have someone stalking you?

- if you were afraid to leave your house?

- if someone stole your idea?

- to have someone stalking you?

- if you were afraid to leave your house?

- if someone stole your idea?

- to be an angel?

- to have anything in the world for one day?

- to get fired from a job?

- to be upside down in a yellow submarine?

- if everyone but you disappeared?

- to work in a greenhouse?

- to be bitten by an animal?

- to be the director of a movie?

- to spill a tray of food in front of a large crowd?

- to be on the staff of your favorite magazine?

- to wear shorts all the time?

- to fall in love at first sight?

- to communicate with your eyelids?

- to be adopted by a family of a different race?

- if you could feel another person's pain?

What would it be like. . .?. . .?. . .?

- to eat a cactus?
- to be snubbed?
- to live on Mars?
- to get at least one hug a day?
- to wash your car in the rain?
- to have your own apartment?
- to be the tallest person in the world?
- to have a book on the best seller list?
- to build a car from scratch?
- to never take a test?
- to get stuck in the middle of a water slide?
- to have amnesia?
- to meet an alien?
- to attend to the king/queen everyday?
- to get up every morning for work at 5:00 a.m.?
- to be the man in the moon?
- to ski on an expert slope?

- to be a street-corner hot dog vendor?

- to grow up with wolves?

- to work on a cattle ranch?

- to walk on crutches for two weeks?

- to add any one thing to your surroundings?

- to knit your own sweater?

- to communicate without words?

- to be divorced?

- if you didn't have to eat?

- to walk across America?

- to live your life in an elevator?

- to never get a hug from anyone?

- to live in a mountain cabin in the winter?

- to own a beach-front condo?

- to be the shortest person in the world?

- if you were a teen idol?

- to discover a lost city?

- if there were no more tests?

- to lose your swimsuit while swimming?

- to be colorblind?

- to discover a bomb?

- if Scotty beamed you up?

- to go bankrupt?

- to live inside a computer chip?

- to discover a famous shipwreck?

- to be a Pharaoh?

- if your best friend was an animal?

- to be a professional perfume tester?

- to get Gatorade® dumped all over you?

- to stand in a line for 45 minutes?

- to trade places with your parents?

- to eat sushi?

- to go to heaven?

- to live in the dark?

- to be buried in the sand up to your neck?

- to walk a tight wire 50 feet in the air?

- to be Bill Gates?

- to build your own boat?

- to go through school without paper?

- to be an inch tall?

- to be alive inside another person?

- if computers never existed?

- to press a button to launch an atomic bomb?

- to shoot an animal?

- to be a wardrobe consultant?

- to be a miner?

- to watch a baby being born?

- to design your own neon light?

- to do the work but not get the credit?

What would it be like . . . ? . . . ? . . . ?

- to always wear a hat?

- to trade places with your brother/sister?

- to discover a new land?

- to never be embarrassed?

- to eat with chopsticks?

- to go rock climbing?

- to live in poverty?

- to decide the fate of a convicted criminal?

- if you could never hug anyone?

- to be able to walk on water?

- to have your own charge card?

- if you had hair nine feet long?

- to be Bill Gates's child?

- to save the world?

- to earn a varsity letter?

- to body surf waves over eight feet tall?

- to be God?

- to dissect a human body?

- to choose between curtain #1 and $1,000?

- to earn $100,000 a year?

- to be in constant pain?

- if dreams were gateways?

- to soar like an owl?

- to have a job repairing highways?

- to witness a crime?

- to create a masterpiece?

- to have parents of different races?

- to hike down into a dormant volcano?

- to live with you?

- to be featured on 60 Minutes®?

- to discover a cure for AIDS?

- to camp out in the snow?

- if someone said you were beautiful/handsome?

- to rescue someone from a fire?

- if you knew you were going to die today?

- to see what a postage stamp sees?

- to be a doctor who loses a patient?

- if looks were all that mattered?

- to stick your head in the mouth of a lion?

- to be a lifeguard?

- to be a master chess player?

- to be a pallbearer in a funeral?

- to help deliver a baby in a taxi?

- if your only clothes were hand-me-downs?

- if there were no written communication?

- if you could choose your family?

- to feel no happiness?

- to order everthing on the Web?

- to be lost?

- to live in the White House?

- to get married in a hot air balloon?

- to go skinny dipping?

- to own a solar-powered car?

- to wear braces on your teeth?

- to get the red carpet treatment?

- to write an autobiography?

- to never have to study and get all A's?

- to go cliff diving?

- to be a senior citizen?

- to make your own laws?

- if you could see clearly in the dark?

- to be on the barter system?

- to devote your life to the poor and sick?

- to go beyond time and space?

- to be a hydrogen atom?

- to save a stranded baby bird?

- to be a famous dog trainer?

- to work in an animal shelter?

- to do community service?

- to spend a weekend in a penthouse suite?

- to have an identical twin?

- to walk across Africa?

- to live in a world without money?

- to get married in Las Vegas?

- to wear dentures?

- to be Miss Universe/Mr. Universe?

- to appear in a commercial?

- to go ballroom dancing?

- if there were no laws?

- to spend the night in a haunted house?

- to cross a picket line?

- to live in a stress free world?

- to encounter a bear in the wilderness?

- to be a lion tamer?

- to clean other people's houses for a living?

- to be drafted?

- to leave your body to science?

- to fall in the mud with your clothes on?

- if we communicated through headphones?

- if there were no families?

- to feel no guilt?

- to eat a worm?

- to lose your way?

- to live off the land?

- to have no responsibilities?

- to be kissed by a monkey?

- to climb a 70 foot tree?

- to own a jet ski?

- to change one of your facial features?

What would it be like. . . ? . . . ? . . . ? . . . ?

- if someone asked you for your autograph?

- to create your own candy bar?

- to take any subjects you wanted in school?

- to ride in a glider?

- to be liquid?

- to find a winning lottery ticket?

- to be the only survivor of a plane crash?

- to be walking in a picket line?

- to be a throw away?

- without a conscience?

- to be a sequoia tree?

- to milk a cow?

- to be a bullfighter?

- to be a school bus driver?

- to be stuck in an elevator for 24 hours?

- to be renamed on your 21st birthday?

- to be a member of the perfect family?

- to hike for a week in Antarctica?

- to live on your own island?

- if your hair turned gray overnight?

- to have a building named after you?

- to invent a game?

- to be a Buddhist monk?

- to change any one rule?

- to be on a sinking ship?

- to be a professional dog walker?

- to fire a machine gun?

- to work in an assisted-living center?

- to go to a space camp?

- to walk across Russia?

- if you were raised in a commune setting?

- to be mistaken for a celebrity?

- if you discovered a genie in a bottle?

what would it be like. . .?. . .?. . .?

- to drive in a monster truck rally?

- to make the trek to Mecca?

- to spend a week with…?

- if you could contact one person after you died?

- to be threatened by a bully?

- if your fantasy became a reality?

- to be an adult?

- to dissect a frog?

- to be a bodyguard to the president?

- to choose any job you wanted?

- to help with Habitat for Humanity®?

- to have a bodyguard?

- if you didn't own shoes?

- if you couldn't communicate for a week?

- to repay your parents?

- to feel no pain?

- to be your worst enemy?

- to attend a computer camp?

- to live in a penthouse?

- to get stood up by a date?

- to fall out of a tree?

- to own your own restaurant?

- to be in the headlines tomorrow?

- if you couldn't smell?

- to make a movie of your life?

- if you got held back a year in school?

- to visit with your favorite sports star?

- to be a genius?

- if you didn't make mistakes?

- to be released from prison after ten years?

- to ride a subway to and from work everyday?

- to swim on the back of a whale?

- to be a member of the news media?

- to be a diamond cutter?

- to rent out a movie theatre for one night?

- to have no hope?

- to play flute in the forest by a stream?

- to dress up as Santa Claus?

- if you couldn't listen to music for a year?

- to pay rent to your parents?

- to be the underdog?

- to eat every meal with your hands?

- to try to make everybody happy?

- to be home alone watching a scary movie?

- to spend a day in the city of your choice?

- to live in a trash can?

- to be asked out on a date?

- to be caught in a tornado?

- to own a television station?

- to testify before the Senate?

- if all you knew was the family farm?

- to be taller?

- to have a statue made of you?

- to win an Oscar®?

- to be in a school without desks?

- to hold a black belt in a martial art?

- to go fly a kite?

- to be a friend of Robin Hood?

- to not be touched by another living thing?

- not to have any form of government?

- to be a satellite?

- to live on disability?

- to have to depend on medication to stay alive?

- if Jesus had never been born?

- to be a cobbler?

- to be a radio talk-show host?

What would it be like... ? ... ? ... ?

- to visit a morgue?

- to stay overnight in an airport?

- to wear a tie everyday?

- without music?

- to be a snitch?

- if we didn't use animals as a food source?

- to feel proud of yourself?

- if families always lived together?

- to never fit in?

- to journey to the center of the earth?

- to walk across India?

- to live in your car?

- to ask someone out on a date?

- to see a live active volcano?

- to ride into the sunset?

- to own ten acres of land?

- to have no thumbs?

- if someone wrote a song about you?

- to miss your high school graduation?

- to discover life on a new planet?

- if all electronic games were banned?

- to be a plant and always stay in one place?

- if you never needed any sleep?

- to have a clone of yourself?

- to have your name on an office door?

- to sell door to door?

- to clean up your act?

- to be an immortal?

- to be put into a zoo?

- to be an Olympic gymnast?

- to be an umpire?

- to pose nude for an art class?

- to experience weightlessness?

?

What would it be like. . . ?. . . ?. . . ?. . . ?

- to stay overnight on the street?

- if no one wore shoes?

- to talk with your hands?

- to have a parent in prison?

- to be sad all the time?

- if there were no pizza?

- to go to the Hawaiian Islands?

- to grow up on an army base?

- to go on a blind date?

- to be snowbound in a tent?

- to have your own car?

- to be able to breath underwater unaided?

- to be a superhero?

- to set a world record?

- to go back to school at 40?

- to dribble a basketball across America?

- to be Santa Claus?

- to walk through walls?

- if we all looked alike?

- to frolic?

- to work in customer service?

- to be an escape artist?

- to live on the bottom of the ocean?

- to catch somebody in the act?

- to live by candlelight for a week?

- to spend one day as an animal?

- to be a weather person (meteorologist)?

- to inform the police of a friend's crime?

- to live to be 100?

- if there were no such thing as underwear?

- if you couldn't read?

- if one of your parents was a police officer?

- to have a fear of crowds?

- to become allergic to your favorite food?

- to ride a motorcycle across the U.S?

- to live in a biosphere for one year?

- to have your own home?

- to have your own home?

- to be extremely underweight?

- if your kiss turned someone into a frog?

- to be the vice president?

- without sports?

- to be a character in a book?

- to awaken from a coma after five years?

- to be in a reality TV show?

- to have one magical power?

- to sell door-to-door?

- to be a storyteller?

- to live with someone you were afraid of?

- to be a hamster?

- to teach a class of your peers?

- to be a famous chef?

- to talk to someone from the future?

- if the drinking age changed to 25?

- if all women stayed home?

- to wear the same clothes everyday?

- without books?

- to never have to do chores at home?

- to have a fear of heights?

- to get a pie in the face?

- to live in a castle?

- to travel the country in a mobile home?

- to kiss your favorite movie star?

- to experience an earthquake?

- to have your own horse?

- if you couldn't hear?

?

What would it be like. . . ? . . . ? . . . ? . . . ?

- to act on your favorite television show?

- to invent a new form of transportation?

- to work all day and go to night school?

- if all sports were coed?

- to be immortal?

- to switch places with someone?

- if the world ran out of gas?

- if you had to work in the family business?

- to be a white buffalo?

- to live by faith?

- to care for a baby all day, every day?

- if animals made no sound?

- to be a master violinist?

- to run out of ideas?

- to receive a large package in the mail?

- to give blood?

- to wear a uniform everyday?

- to have a fear of the dark?

- if we communicated only through music?

- to have triplets born into your family today?

- to eat a sugarless diet?

- to go to military school?

- to live in nursing home?

- if you had to greet everyone with a kiss?

- to reach the top of the highest mountain?

- to own a sports team?

- if you couldn't see?

- to be a favorite?

- to win a trophy?

- if there were no school?

- to parachute out of a plane?

- to be a friend?

- if everyone in the world were female?

What would it be like. . .?. . .?. . .?:

- to be granted just one wish?
- if there was no minimum wage?
- to live in a glass house?
- to get your act together?
- to hear voices in your mind?
- to rescue a cat from a tree?
- to be a baby sitter?
- to be robbed?
- to tell people your story?
- to have nightmares every night?
- if we had to wear family uniforms?
- to be fluent in all languages?
- to be in a family with ten children?
- to share something you are proud of?
- to eat at a restaurant for every meal?
- to travel in a submarine?
- to move in with your grandparents?

- to be in love?

- to be lost in the wilderness?

- to be owned by another human being?

- if you lost your voice completely?

- to be the best?

- to build your own robot?

- to attend school in a one room schoolhouse?

- to go SCUBA diving?

- to be free?

- to be shot from a cannon?

- to be confined indoors for six months?

- if you could have any job you wanted?

- to be a blankie (someone's beloved blanket)?

- to have instant replay anytime, anyplace?

- to be sentenced to death?

- to swim with a dolphin?

what would it be like...?...?...?

- to work in a restroom?

- if your best friend told one of your secrets?

- to give away everything you owned?

- to design your own clothing?

- if you couldn't speak?

- to find out that Darth Vader is your father?

- to get rid of your biggest fear?

- to have your cake and eat it too?

- to go on a jungle safari?

- to be stranded on an island by yourself?

- to live like the Jetsons®?

- to be loved unconditionally?

- to lose all that you own in a tornado?

- to own a club?

- if your belly button was your mouth?

- if everyone knew who you were?

- to discover a cure for the common cold?

- if you weren't allowed to go to school?

- to be a cheerleader?

- to be invisible?

- to be without gravity?

- to escape from time for a day?

- to have your own business cards?

- to travel on a river boat down the Nile?

- without kindness?

- to be a kamikaze pilot?

- to be a bird?

- to be a train conductor?

- to lose your wallet?

- to join and be accepted by any group?

- if you had to wear a space suit everyday?

- to have your own website?

- to do everything with your family?

What would it be like. . . ? . . . ? . . . ?

- if you couldn't stop laughing?

- to pack your own lunch everyday?

- to win an all-expense-paid, month-long trip?

- if you had to move every two years?

- to be loved by everyone?

- to jump into ice water?

- to own your own business?

- to have no arms or legs?

- to have famous parents?

- if you won $10,000 but had to give it away?

- without electricity?

- to be stranded at sea in a life raft?

- to be the principal of an inner city school?

- to make the winning score in the big game?

- to make your dreams real?

- if your parents chose your vocation at birth?

- to be a flight attendant?

- to be in orbit?

- to float through the blood stream?

- to be a mountain lion?

- to be a famous artist?

- to have a best friend?

- to do one thing you are not allowed to do?

- to have your own mobile phone?

- to wear a gas mask every time you go outside?

- to be the perfect daughter/son?

- if everyone was afraid of you?

- without snack food at the movies?

- to travel in a yacht?

- to live in a teepee?

- to get stood up at your wedding?

- without flowers?

- to have cosmetic surgery?

What would it be like . . . ? . . . ? . . . ? . . . ?:

- to be a columnist for a big city newspaper?

- to give away a billion dollars?

- to go to boarding school?

- to miss the winning shot in the big game?

- to take back one bad thing you did?

- to find a buried treasure?

- to be Batman®?

- to be given a puppy?

- to be a secret agent?

- to be the MC at the Oscars?

- to own a motorcycle?

- to wear formal clothing all the time?

- to be without a telephone?

- if children were taken from their parents

   at birth and raised in group homes?

- if vegetables were our only food source?

- to have someone play a practical joke on you?

- to go to a nude beach?

- if you had to live in a giant plastic bubble?

- if someone proposed to you?

- if money grew on trees?

- if everyone looked alike?

- to be a movie critic?

- to know everyone in the whole world?

- if you could trade places with your teacher?

- to ride in a bobsled?

- to attend a summer sports camp?

- to be part of the Lewis & Clark Expedition?

- to be charged for a crime you didn't commit?

- to relive one day of your life?

- to be my friend?

- to be a fish?

- to be a baggage handler at an airport?

What would it be like. . . ? . . . ? . . . ? . . . ? :

- to be a pro tennis player?

- to build a float for the Rose Bowl Parade?

- if the sun were blue?

- to go through a car wash with the top down?

- if your best friend was terminally ill?

- if insects were our only source of food?

- to live in an orphanage?

- to live in a tree house?

- to receive a roses from a secret admirer?

- to have wings?

- if you were spoken to by God?

- if you were president for one day?

- to be a teacher's favorite student?

- to ride over a waterfall in a kayak?

- to have cars with wings?

- to trade lives with someone else?

- to get caught out in a thunderstorm?

- to be sent to camp every summer?

- to be a dog?

- to be an indentured sevant?

- to work in a cookie store?

- to wake up everyday in the afternoon?

- to find out you had a terminal illness?

- to be in a foster family?

- to eat the same food everyday?

- to go on a picnic every Friday?

- to build your own tree house?

- to have a new last name?

- if the weather was always 72°and sunny?

- to be strong?

- if you were mistaken for a goddess/god?

- to win the lottery?

- to wear (not wear) a uniform to school?

- to go snowmobiling?

- if all drugs were legal?

- to have the ability to see into the future?

- if time stopped?

- to skin a deer?

- to work in a nursing home?

- to read the newspaper everyday?

- to say something nice about yourself?

- to live with a different family?

- to be a camera man for action news?

- to grow and prepare all of your own food?

- to go on a cattle drive?

- to live on the Starship Enterprise®?

- to fall in love at first sight?

- if grass were red?

- to be physically handicapped?

- to be on a game show?

- if you could bring one person back to life?

- to cheat on a test?

- to jump off a cliff?

- to be in a world without deodorant?

- to meet someone just like you?

- if there were no such thing as memory?

- to wake up and be an adult/child?

- to be tickled pink?

- to be my teacher?

- to find a stray dog?

- to work on a cruise ship?

- if things were different?

- to meditate for an hour everyday?

- to build a house with no power tools?

- if your parents broke a promise?

- to drive a car in a demolition derby?

- if you could only eat once a day?

- to be lost in a foreign country?

- if everyone lived in apartments?

- to get a "love" note?

- if wood didn't burn?

- to be mentally handicapped?

- to be born a boy, but raised as a girl?

- to create and run your own museum?

- to go to school all year long?

- to be your family pet?

- to be the best skateboarder in the world?

- if your skin changed colors?

- to be angry all the time?

- to discover a new species of animal?

- to be a private detective?

- to meet someone who has the same name?

- to "wander off the beaten path"?

- to stay out as long as you wanted?

- to taste test for the Jelly Belly Bean®Co.?

- to have a new sister/brother?

- if you couldn't taste anything?

- to go on a mission trip outside of the U.S?

- to be a medical doctor?

- without seasons?

- to relocated with a new identity?

- to be beautiful/handsome?

- to be the heroine/hero?

- to be a playwright?

- to be a foreign exchange student?

- to go snowboarding?

- if there were no mirrors?

- to be abducted by aliens?

- to fly on a magic carpet?

?

What would it be like. . .?. . .?. . .?

- to be a refugee?

- if you could change things with a wink?

- to own a music/video game store?

- to shoot an animal?

- to be a radio DJ?

- to be a scapegoat?

- if we only had cold water showers?

- to have a secret hideout?

- to be a lawyer?

- to have you for a child?

- to not eat for a week?

- to fly to the moon?

- to work on a farm?

- to be a runaway?

- to be a parent, work, and go to school?

- if our only source of water were rain?

- if you couldn't walk?

- to be famous?

- to design your own billboard?

- to go to military school?

- to be voted the "most valuable player"?

- to tell a group of peers your story?

- to travel by pogo stick?

- to be the opposite gender?

- to know that someone trusted you?

- if you could communicate with animals?

- to be a dentist?

- if everything we used was handmade?

- to have an outhouse for your toilet?

- to be all by yourself for a day?

- to work at a library?

- to choose your own chores?

- to be born a girl, but raised as a boy?

- to hike for a week in the desert?

- to be a police officer?

- to live in a monastery?

- if there were no such thing as marriage?

- without the sun?

- if you couldn't use your hands?

- to be infamous?

- to host your own talk show?

- to study abroad for a year?

- to be the world's fastest human?

- if everything you touched turned to gold?

- if tooting in public was against the law?

- to travel in a time machine?

- to be the heir apparent to $10,000,000?

- if we didn't have cats?

- to be happy all the time?

- to be an elephant trainer?

- to exercise for 3 hours a day?

- without glass?

- to be all alone in the world for a day?

- to be in a musical band?

- to find out today that you were adopted?

- without hate?

- to go dog sledding?

- to clean the windows of a skyscraper?

- to live in an artist colony?

- to marry a prince/princess?

- if it snowed feathers?

- to lose all your hair?

- to be on the cover of Sports Illustrated®?

- to sell your story to a movie maker?

- if only the rich could afford to go to school?

- to go paintballing?

- to cross the country in a covered wagon?

- to play the bad guy/girl in a movie?

- to be an Ivy League graduate?

- to be a butterfly?

- to bag groceries for a living?

- without covers?

- to start a club?

- to be by yourself at home for a week?

- to be a missionary worker?

- to never have to clean your room?

- if you were unable to taste sweet?

- to go to Disneyland®?

- to be a fire fighter?

- to live in a one room sod house?

- to receive a diamond ring?

- to have bad acne?

- to be on the cover of People Magazine®?

- to decide what was shown on television?

- if you created a new sport?

- if your horoscope were accurate everyday?

- if things always went exactly as planned?

- to take credit for what someone else did?

- to be an ant?

- to be an active member of Green Peace®?

- to move from a third world country to the U.S?

- to lie to your best friend?

- to be a model?

- to pick new parents?

- if your secrets were exposed?

- to be a member of a gang?

- to churn butter?

- to travel across Europe on a train?

- to be a butler/maid?

What would it be like. . .?. . .?. . .?

- to live on a different planet?

- to have a secret admirer?

- to be extremely overweight?

- to be a famous magician?

- to solve the unemployment problem?

- to complete a triathlon?

- if every word started with the letter "B"?

- to have to wear a tracking device?

- to live with a person who is 100 yrs. old?

- to be a house cat?

- to be a trash collector?

- to donate an organ that saved a life?

- without television?

- to be your parent's caregiver?

- to be a nurse?

- to have rich parents?

- to be served breakfast in bed?

- to sail around the world?

- to be a professional golfer?

- to live in a log cabin?

- to be infatuated?

- if you had no hair?

- to be the ruler of a small country?

- to have your picture on the front of a tabloid?

- to win a gold medal in the Olympics?

- to attend a big Hollywood party?

- if we all had what we needed no more, no less?

- if you never had to shop again?

- to think like a computer?

- to create your own animal?

- to sleep during the day and be awake at night?

- without cars?

- to work on an oil rig?

What would it be like . . . ? . . . ? . . . ?

- not to have any private space?

- to be in a pie-eating contest?

- to travel in a blimp?

- to be a chauffeur?

- to live in an underwater city?

- to be obsessed?

- to wake up and be a different race?

- if you were a movie star?

- to be voted the most attractive person alive?

- to be a famous musician?

- to discover a new land?

- to make your own laws?

- if you knew everything?

- to discover a secret passage?

- to lose your best friend?

- to speak to a large group of your peers?

- to be a Catholic nun/priest?

- to have a disabled brother or sister?

- to ride in a hot air balloon?

- if it rained everyday?

- if we ALL had hairy armpits?

- to direct a movie?

- to spend a week with the President?

- if we ran out of land for cemeteries?

- to lose a winning lottery ticket?

- if the FBI had unlimited access?

- to stay in jail overnight?

- to work at a fast food restaurant?

- to be an only child?

- to ride in the space shuttle?

- to live in a cave?

- to change one thing about the way you look?

- to have the energy of Tigger?

- to have a street named after you?

- to be dating a movie star?

- to use an amusement park for a day?

- to control the world?

- to find a hundred dollar bill?

- if the government regulated the First

  Amendment?

- to be a stunt person?

- to apologize to everyone you needed to?

- to sail the seven seas?

- to live in Russia?

- to be in a boxing match?

- to run out of gas on a date?

- to be a taxi driver in a big city?

- to be a substitute teacher?

- to not know who your parents were?

- to walk across China?

- to be an all-star wrestler?

- to live in a house with no running water?

- if we couldn't sit down?

- to save someone who was drowning?

- if you were irresistible?

- to witness a robbery?

- to lose everything you owned in a fire?

- to be a psychotherapist?

- to get an allowance for everything you did?

- to be stuck in quicksand?

- to win a Nobel Prize?

- to discover a new civilization?

- without the color white?

- if there were no legal drinking age limit?

- to sleep a night in a graveyard by yourself?

- to drive an armored car?

What would it be like. . .?. . .?. . .?

- to be part of the in-crowd?

- to be alive in another person?

- to drive a tank?

- to save someone who was choking?

- if there were only G-rated movies?

- to be a roadie for your favorite band?

- to ride in a rodeo?

- to be a member of a church youth group?

- to lie to your parents?

- to be a sea captain?

- if you had to fight in a war?

- to be a professional body-builder?

- to live in a cartoon?

- if you woke up and everything you knew
  to this point had only been a dream?

- if you were lost in a cave?

- to make a living as a street musician?

- to live in the mountains?

- to be there for a friend?

- to stay in a hospital overnight?

- if the wish you made on a penny and

  threw into a fountain came true?

- to work as a computer game-tester?

- to move to a new state?

- to never see the out-of-doors?

- to go back in time?

- to be an ambulance driver?

- to live in a harem?

- to be on vacation everyday?

- to write a book?

- to be an animator?

- to be part of the perfect family?

- if we ran out of space?

What would it be like . . . ? . . . ? . . . ?

- to go bungee jumping?

- to drive a race car?

- to be a minister?

- if we were all normal?

- if you were pulled over by a police officer?

- to mud wrestle?

- without anesthesia?

- to witness a car accident?

- to drive an eighteen-wheeler for a job?

- to backpack across the Grand Canyon?

- to be a performer in a traveling circus?

- to be a "test tube" baby?

- to forget your wallet on a dinner date?

- to be in a dance troupe that performed
  around the world?

- to cut off your arm for unlimited wealth?

- to climb the the Statue of Liberty?

- to fly a plane?

- to give your life for someone else?

- if someone said you were stupid?

- to have a paper route?

- to have nine lives?

- if you told your best friend's secret?

- to be on television?

- to get your finger stuck in your nose?

- to be in a parade?

- to work in a toy factory?

- to communicate with your guardian angel?

- to look out over Paris from the Eiffel Tower?

- if everyone you knew forgot your birthday?

- to have a fairy godmother/father?

- to be the pitcher for a major league team?

- to do your own thing?

What would it be like... ? ... ? ... ? ... ?

- if everything in the world were yellow?

- to have all your belongings stolen?

- to meet a king?

- to teach an adult something you're good at?

- to be the quarterback on a football team?

- to pre-plan your funeral?

- if there were no secrets?

- if your brother/sister was a movie star?

- to work in a factory?

- if no one lied?

- to go ahead into the future?

- to devote your life to a cause?

- to trust yourself?

- to "rock the boat"?

- to have no fear?

- to be old?

- to open a treasure chest?

- to escape from the real world?

- to sail away?

- to realize a dream?

- to have fun?

- to be yourself?

- to be satisfied?

- to make a difference?

- to have to choose between money and love?

- to have to choose which parent to live with?

- to feel safe?

- to have enough?

- to have to decide your own punishment?

- to go camping with your friends for two weeks?

- to be a minister?

- to give up your favorite bad habit?

- to be in charge of the weather everyday?

- to be a martyr?

- to decided whether or not to declare war?

- to be a potter?

- to bloom in the spring and die in the fall?

- to live in a cottage by the sea?

- to fall asleep every time you sit down?

- to own a vineyard?

- to be the sole survivor of a race of people?

- to give up?

- to discover gold in the Yukon?

- to find that your parents read your diary?

- to make a documentary on your high school?

- to be a mime in Central Park?

- to be a flower child of the 60's?

- to be a mermaid/man?

- to be a single parent?

- if your nose grew every time you told a lie?

- to be responsible?

- to believe in magic?

- to stop living by the clock?

- to be unique?

- to never make comparisons?

- to build a sand castle on the beach?

- to be on the ark with Noah and all the animals?

- to stay in bed all day?

- to stop worrying?

- to marry someone like me?

- to be down to your last dollar?

- to face the facts?

- to go to a luau?

- to stutter?

- to be a member of high society?

- to be a clown?

What would it be like. . .?. . .?. . .?

- to belong?

- to live in a refugee camp?

- if you were your best friend?

- to be raised by your grandparents?

- to be your father?

- to be your mother?

- to be a hermit?

- to be an angel?

- if there were no walls or fences?

- if no one owned anything?

- if we were allowed only one friend?

- if you didn't care what other people thought?

- to be a gardener?

- to have a secret identity?

- to be a military chaplain?

- if no one cared?

- to write an advice column?

• to write over a thousand

"What Would It Be Like...?'s?

?

?

add some questions of your own...

add some questions of your own...

What would it be like...?...?...?

?

add some questions of your own...

Aknowledgements

We give our utmost thanks to Mary Sue Cavert and
Susana's advisory & kids for their fun contributions.
And as always, to the wonderful support and effort
put in by the Wood 'N' Barnes Publishing staff.

Aknowledgements

Activity Idea from:
"Games (and other stuff) for Teachers"

Procedure: Clear out the center of the room as much as possible and form a nice big circle with your group.

You will ask the players to choose one of the two characteristics from each statement you are going to read. If they are more like the first characteristic, have them step inside the circle. If they are more like the second characteristic, have them stay where they are as part of the circle. Leave a little time between each statement to give the students a chance to see who else is standing with them. Play along with them, by just stepping in and out of the circle as you read.

That's the simple gist. We like to use this activity as our introduction to the process of active learning (getting up and moving around). We keep it simple the first time with a little processing after. Down the road we can use this activity again to bring out more personal perspectives and discussions.

Introduction

The first couple of hundred "Are You More Like...." questions appeared in the book, "Games (and other stuff) for Teachers" by Chris Cavert and Laurie Frank. We had such a great response to the first set of questions and had so much fun thinking of them, we just couldn't stop there. The latest Pocket Prompter has 1001 "Are You More Like..." ponderables that can help open up discussions to many different topics. While you've got your group pondering keep in mind the questions are also useful for personality identification and like/dislike elimination. This book is also a useful ice breaking tool for groups of any age.

You will have a great deal of fun with these questions. When using them, try to encourage the participants to think more about the characteristics of the items. Younger groups will often just choose the item they like best-nothing wrong with that! Do whatever works best for your group. Because this book was created for such a wide variety of audiences we have bold typed the questions that may be more effective for older participants or produce more complex thought. Feel free to add your own ideas. Just don't forget to keep the spirit of fun in all that you do.

Are You More Like...

wacky or weird?

noon or midnight?

a flower or a weed?

Are You More Like......

a gallery or a museum?

a crossword puzzle or a word search?

a bloom or a bud?

hard boiled or scrambled eggs?

the coffee table or the kitchen table?

insatiable or satisfied?

a slide or a swing?

head lights or tail lights?

a trick or a treat?

a stander or a sitter?

a pink flamingo or a lawn gnome?

express or standard?

auditory or visual?

an action or a reaction?

a yo-yo or a spinning top?

a country farm or a neighborhood?

a ladder or a pole?

the ocean or the mountains?

a bracelet, a necklace, or a ring?

cash or a gift certificate?

figure skating or speed skating?

aluminum or wood?

black or white?

a lemon or a lime?

the mast or the rudder?

the escalator or the stairs?

up front or out back?

a sponge or a strainer?

imminent or possible?

cardboard or paper?

a cat or a dog?

calm or hyper?

a hot tub or a sauna?

the United States or a foreign country?

evaporation or solidification?

A's or B's?

fur or scales?

a country or a state?

an almanac or a biography?

the defense or the offense?

a cause or an effect?

spots or stripes?

Ballet or Hip-Hop?

a fountain or a waterfall?

influential or listless?

a bottle or a can?

a small group or a large group?

touch, smell, taste, sight or sound?

Tupperware© or Ziplocks©?

mass or space?

a dictionary or a thesaurus?

a night shirt or a knight's suit of armor?

mind or matter?

an explorer or a settler?

boxers or briefs?

flats or high heels?

extraordinary or normal?

"a change of pace" or "the same old same old"?

the roots or the limbs?

a cable or a clamp?

nutricious or delicious?

a passenger or a pilot?

sunshine or moon light?

Shakespeare or Dr. Suess?

an aisle or a window seat?

a kaleidoscope or a telescope?

the cheese or the macaroni?

the table of contents or the index?

a hard cover book or a paperback book?

the desert or the rain forest?

the arrow or the target?

a door or a window?

a China cabinet or a trophy case?

to be or not to be?

a bird's song or a frog's croak?

heads or tails?

the landing or the take-off?

a bun or a loaf?

married or single?

an animal lover or a people lover?

energy or calm?

an M.V.P. or a V.I.P.?

a drawing or a painting?

a paramedic or a police officer?

a nine iron or a putter?

the fixture or the light?

a buyer or a maker?

the front porch or the back porch?

fleece or leather?

clockwise or counterclockwise?

an arrival or a departure?

a café or a deli?

air waves or wires?

please or thank you?

a TV dinner or fast food?

by the clock or by the moment?

an apartment or a house?

liquid soap or powdered soap?

a coat or a vest?

a coconut or a pineapple?

the kitchen or the living room?

in or out?

the door or the doorknob?

the ball or the chain?

a ball or a strike?

economy or luxury?

a cold shower or a hot shower?

a sitcom or a drama?

a giver or a receiver?

a boomerang or a Frisbee©?

inflated or reduced?

a magazine or a newspaper?

a candle or a flashlight?

a trash can or a recycling bin?

a movie or prime time?

an address or a phone number?

the ugly duckling or the swan?

socks or shoes?

"enough is enough" or "grin and bear it"?

the Equator or the North Pole?

plain or peanut?

a garden or a playground?

french toast or pancakes?

a carpenter or a plumber?

a carport or a garage?

ground beef or a T-bone?

a fruit or a vegetable?

a copy or an original?

an air conditioner or a furnace?

air mail or an E-mail?

a carpet or a rug?

anything or something?

rock, paper or scissors?

a fan or a vacuum cleaner?

a story or a song?

shy or cautious?

baking or grilling?

Battleship© or Tic Tac Toe©?

a cough or a sneeze?

a kite or a sailboat?

East or West?

Biology or Geology?

a country road or the highway?

a trickster or a truth teller?

loud or quiet?

a mover or a shaker?

the center or the edge?

a museum or a circus?

an adjustment or a revision?

place mats or a table cloth?

an expert or novice?

a plain cone or waffle cone?

the green or the rough?

a chalkboard or a dry erase board?

a guest or a host?

the cup or the saucer?

traditional or contemporary?

a bagel or a slice of bread?

shoes or socks?

full service or self service?

a Bell Boy or a Bus Boy?

affordable or expensive?

a daisy or a rose?

listening or reading?

the Empire State Building or the Great Wall of China?

a catcher or a pitcher?

lobster or shrimp?

excited or reserved?

an oven or a refrigerator?

action or suspense?

a cushion or a pillow?

art or music?

punt, pass or kick?

the land or the sea?

aluminum foil or plastic wrap?

the commuter train or the HOV lane?

a paint gun or a water gun?

chocolate or strawberries?

an egineer or a mechanic?

American or Swiss cheese?

consensus or majority?

the hider or the seeker?

an amusement park or a water park?

rain water or well water?

fireworks or a laser show?

rapids or ripples?

a bath or a shower?

diet or regular?

a reaction or a response?

a hill or a mountain?

a window or a mirror?

honey or sugar?

a student or a teacher?

a box fan or a ceiling fan?

a honey bee or a bumble bee?

a jump or a dive?

a gift-bag or gift wrap?

the young or the old?

an event or a mediation?

a jukebox or a music box?

a belcher or a passer?

a taco or a tamale?

a hand written or typed letter?

stern or lenient?

the outdoors or the indoors?

a cruise or an expedition?

a bikini or a one piece?

an opera or a rodeo?

a dollar or a penny?

a private school or public school?

a cherry or a lemon?

accidental or intentional?

a moon or a star?

a ferris wheel or a merry-go-round?

a broom or a vacuum?

a field or a forest?

a pickup truck or a van?

letters or numbers?

delayed or en route?

a bubble bath or mineral bath?

a wish or an idea?

a mountain climber or a spelunker?

simple or complicated?

the book cover or book pages?

a pier or a raft?

conform or differ?

wheat or white bread?

an ax or a chainsaw?

cheesecake or Jello®?

the inside or the outside?

Baby blue or Navy blue?

scientific or theological?

freedom or slavery?

a screen door or wooden door?

a blimp or a submarine?

drifting or steering?

a signature or a seal?

jacks or marbles?

a convertible or a minivan?

a jester or a king?

abbreviated or expanded?

a buyer or a seller?

jelly or peanut butter?

the washer or the dryer?

a bedroom or a loft?

check in or carry on?

everybody or somebody?

Karate or Thai Chi?

Bluegrass or Opera?

a preacher or a teacher?

a hot springs or a Jacuzzi©?

humble or proud?

the library or a bookstore?

brave or afraid?

Bob Cratchet or Mr. Scrooge?

pasta or rice?

an ear or an eye?

an order or a request?

an alien or a native?

coffee or tea?

an organ or a piano?

the forest or a tree?

a camping chair or a hammock?

a forward or a goalie?

potato chips or pretzels?

art or mathematics?

doubles or singles?

England or Australia?

an experience or a metaphor?

a paintbrush or a roller?

a banner or a flag?

deodorant or antiperspirant?

racquet ball or tennis?

crayons or paint?

adding or subtracting?

a best seller book or a second hand book?

a desktop or a laptop computer?

stars or stripes?

barrel racing or bull riding?

a stander or a leaner?

multiple choice questions or an essay?

Los Angeles or New York?

the bowling ball or the bowling pin?

an eraser or White-Out©?

stocks or mutual funds?

a card or a note?

the cucumber or the pickle?

a lighter or a match?

a shopper or a sightseer?

a witness or a victim?

a lighthouse or an outhouse?

even or irregular?

"Out of the blue" or "Out in the open"?

a cloth napkin or paper napkins?

"An eye for an eye" or "Turn the other cheek"?

lined or unlined paper?

brakes or downshifting?

off or on?

a hotel or a motel?

patient or restless?

a tourist or a resident?

a grin or a laugh?

"break even" or "go for broke"?

a pocket watch or a wrist watch?

exceed or lag?

salt or pepper?

depth or width?

country music or rap music?

peppermint or cinnamon?

the basement or the attic?

catsup or mustard?

a gas fireplace or wood-burning fireplace?

salt or sugar?

a ball cap or a visor?

an editor or a writer?

an egg timer or an hour glass?

automatic or manual transmission?

a picnic or a restaurant?

a happy birthday or a Happy New Year?

down or up?

sandals or tennis shoes?

a clothing store or a toy store?

an amateur or a veteran?

blackjack or the slot machines?

downtown or uptown?

masking tape or scotch tape?

roller blades or roller skates?

Twister© or Scrabble©?

a highlight or an underline?

Velcro© or zippers?

buttered or plain popcorn?

an explanation or a complication?

a vendor or a vending machine?

meatballs or spaghetti?

dirt or grass?

a meeting or a memo?

love or labor?

change or consistency?

mental or physical?

the exterior or the interior?

a boy or a man?

a corporate executive or an entrepreneur?

a fog horn or a light house?

a millionaire or a pauper?

cable or satellite?

blended or stirred?

lip gloss or lip stick?

passive or active?

a choice or a chance?

Big Bird® or Oscar the Grouch®?

cake or cookies?

rope or thread?

the favorite or the underdog?

polo or water polo?

bald or a full head of hair?

a song or a dance?

a pop-up toaster or a toaster oven?

a hard hat or a top hat?

a burger or fried chicken?

the tortoise or the hare?

a Speedo© or trunks?

a belt or suspenders?

exempt or responsible?

gel or mousse?

bubble gum or chewing gum?

a sand trap or a water hazard?

boots or sandals?

an elf or a giant?

stain or varnish?

downhill or slalom skiing?

staying at home or going on vacation?

the bottom or the top?

endless or fixed?

the mud or the sand?

the bow or the arrow?

right brained or left brained?

fishing or hunting?

summers on the beach or winter in the Alps?

a cap or a hat?

international or national?

wacky or weird?

a note or a recording?

the driver or a passenger?

noon or midnight?

an agreement or a debate?

a clock or a wrist watch?

North or South?

a flower or a weed?

a cab or limousine?

a corner or a side?

a follower or a leader?

a mobile phone or a public phone?

carpet or a wooden floor?

"A" or "Z"?

the monkey bars or the swing set?

unique or usual?

a comment or a suggestion?

the Grand Canyon or Pike's Peak?

carry out or delivery?

skim milk or 2%?

a foot or a meter?

a patch work quilt or a stain glass window?

billiards or pinball?

a donkey or a horse?

a garage sale or storage?

drive in or a drive through?

coins or paper money?

the infield or the outfield?

a 35 millimeter camera or a Polaroid?

a bird or a fish?

far or near?

loose leaf or spiral bound paper?

a bumper or a fender?

a square nut or a wing nut?

a bulldozer or a crane?

"hello" or "good-bye"?

trash or treasure?

half empty or half full?

a barbershop or a salon?

a bus or a cab?

expectant or indifferent?

an Opera or a pantomime?

a bus trip or a plane ride?

absorbent or impervious?

lease or own?

comfortable or uneasy?

full price or on special?

french fries or onion rings?

"In the dark" or "In the great wide open"?

parking near the door or away from the door?

an essay or a poem?

a term paper or a project?

an answering machine or caller ID?

cookies or rice cakes?

a paper clip or a rubber band?

the fruit or the vine?

a cardboard box or a plastic container?

jump rope or hopscotch?

a wheel chair or a cane?

an oak or a willow tree?

checkers or chess?

together or apart?

oil or vinegar?

an obstacle or an assistance?

a visitor or a local?

an athelete or a genius?

a castle or a cottage?

the sneak preview or the video?

the future or the past?

a soak or a spin?

skin or bones?

earmuffs or a hat?

soda or water?

a knight or a peasant?

a country club or a night club?

a ladybug or a praying mantis?

dinner or supper?

a story book reader or a story teller?

Are You More Like......

a field or a stream?

a principal or a teacher?

a dot.com or a dot.org?

the train or the track?

a can or a jar?

a finger or a thumb?

morning, noon, or night?

an exit ramp or an on ramp?

biased or fair?

sugar or artificial sweetner?

a fire-cracker or a sparkler?

a photo album or a picture frame?

canines or molars?

an advance or a retreat?

a massage or a whirlpool?

an adverb or a verb?

a clap or a snap?

grass or sand?

an advisor or an encourager?

a planter or a vase?

an export or an import?

work or play?

the back yard or the playground?

a cup or a gallon?

a player or a spectator?

a gulper or a sipper?

a chapter book or a picture book?

a doctor or a nurse?

hamburgers or hotdogs?

the pass or the run?

a cloudy or sunny day?

a baked potato or french-fries?

once or twice?

habitual or sporadic?

a phone call or a telegram?

Morse Code or sign language?

a checking or a savings account?

a tame or a wild horse?

a hanger or a hook?

a tarp or a tent?

Broadway or off-Broadway?

the exception or the rule?

a test or a quiz?

long sleeves or short sleeves?

the defendant or the plaintiff?

the long way home or a short cut?

shy or bold?

bubbles or a balloon?

the foundation or the structure?

ice cream or hot fudge?

concrete or wood?

a scientist or a artist?

the ceiling or the floor?

a four door or two door vehicle?

a doctor or a writer?

fingers or toes?

black & white or color?

a certainty or a quandary?

fragrant or odorless?

a raincoat or an umbrella?

a chain lock or a dead bolt?

a snow angel or snow man?

a new car or a used car?

an announcement or a secret?

man made or organic?

a hiking trail or a sidewalk?

an annoyance or a pleasure?

"Read between the lines" or "Say it like it is"?

the flame or the wax?

ready, willing or able?

The Beatles or Elvis?

disposable or rechargable batteries?

a rectangular table or a round table?

the hook or the line?

a closet or a trunk?

a doer or a thinker?

hand made or industrial?

a passing or a no-passing zone?

corn or wheat?

a believer or a skeptic?

singular or plural?

blunt or subtle?

a nature lover or a sports lover?

a tornado or an earthquake?

the club or the recreation center?

Cleopatra or Joan of Arc?

the President of the U.S. or John Doe?

an entry way or a closet?

designer or second hand?

the fence or the gate?

a bedroom or bathroom?

the moon or the sun?

a door or a floor?

a morning person or night person?

abandoned or inhabited?

a campfire or a fireplace?

gas power or solar power?

"at the line" or "down the line"?

an electric blanket or a quilt?

an actor or a director?

a "Chip on the shoulder" or a "Heart on the sleeve"?

glass or plastic?

an autobiography or a biography?

a 4 wheel drive or 2 wheel drive?

bottled water or tap water?

circles or lines?

mini-golf or 18 holes?

school or vacation?

a circle or a square?

the back or the front?

pants or shorts?

a backhand or forehand?

a cruise or a hike?

a "Jack of all trades" or a specialist?

the back seat or the front seat?

seasonal or year round?

friendly or antagonistic?

the shade or the sun?

blue or green?

the drums or the guitar?

shaken or stirred?

a journal or a tabloid?

a chord or a note?

a duffle bag or a suitcase?

hot sauce or mild sauce?

playing cards or trading cards?

a curl or a wave?

bells or whistles?

Romeo and Juliet or Star Wars©?

an open door or a closed door?

more or less?

a detective or a spy?

cotton or silk?

a Poodle or a Rotweiler?

the key or the lock?

a pen and ink drawing or a finger painting?

the original or the sequel?

ebb or flow?

a hawk or a vulture?

a bull or a bunny?

emotional or rational?

a bully or a nerd?

glue or tape?

a bun or a pony tail?

contacts or glasses?

a basket or shopping cart?

plaid or solids?

Africa or Antartica?

stop or yield?

a green light, a red light, or a yellow light?

a summary or "word-for-word"?

a burden or a breeze?

cupid or the tooth fairy?

a documentary or a safari?

a tree branch or a tree trunk?

skis or a snowboard?

cursive or printing?

A Capella or accompaniment?

a listener or a talker?

an acoustic or electric guitar?

a Picasso or a Renior?

exclusion or inclusion?

paid by the hour or paid by the job?

a slap stick or a stand up comic?

getting what you want or giving in?

a component or a system?

here or there?

candy or popcorn?

a critic or a fan?

a blanket or a sheet?

a ramp or a staircase?

a blink or a wink?

a wash or a wax?

a historical marker or a scenic overlook?

why or why not?

metric or standard?

a diver or a swimmer?

dull or sharp?

caffeinated or decaffeinated?

a sled or skis?

cutting or tearing?

A la Carte or an extra value meal?

a monopoly or an open market?

"All or nothing" or "Take what you can get"?

the post or the sign?

a fiddle or a violin?

infinite or limited?

an elevator or an escalator?

gloves or mittens?

an e-mail or a phone call?

an inner-tube or a raft?

a cassette tape or a CD?

a dialogue or a discussion?

a bow tie or a neck tie?

a scorpion or a snake?

a box or an envelope?

church or a night club?

jeans or khakis?

a gardener or a chef?

a nose ring or a toe ring?

dry goods or perishable?

"every day" or "every now and then"?

carry out or dine in?

King Arthur or Robin Hood?

a dolphin or a shark?

apples or oranges?

an optimist or a pessimist?

an aristocrat or a commoner?

a runner or a walker?

fork, knife or spoon?

a lake or a pool?

a glance or a look?

winning or losing?

a globe or a map?

a landlord or a tenant?

hot or cold cereal?

a drain or a vacuum?

a bush or a tree?

a stapler or a staple?

buttons or snaps?

a Michaelangelo or a Van Gogh?

a letter or a postcard?

family or company?

a canoe or a kayak?

even or odd?

a face lift or wrinkles?

cash or charge?

a time machine or a time capsule?

a dust cloth or a feather duster?

balancing or juggling?

a pen or a pencil?

the accelerator or the brakes?

a counter top or a shelf?

a ball or a bat?

solids or stripes?

the lawn or the garden?

a picker or a pickee?

a glider or a jet?

loose or tight?

a Mac or a PC?

a main course or a side dish?

combat boots or cowboy boots?

a campground or a rest stop?

a marker or a pen?

a manicure or a pedicure?

a chocolate chip cookie or an oatmeal cookie?

an exhale or an inhale?

a one-way trip or round trip?

enough or too much?

a paper clip or a staple?

the lottery or bingo?

a picnic blanket or picnic table?

an expiration or an inspiration?

a car or a truck?

for or against?

the median or the shoulder of the road?

a weekday or weekend?

chance or design?

an aid or an obstacle?

a playground or a stadium?

an extrovert or an introvert?

mild or spicy?

an airport or a bus station?

a map or a compass?

a clown or an acrobat?

the head lines or the bottom line?

a big screen or a compact screen?

Dr. Martin Luther King or Neil Armstrong?

exaggerated or underestimated?

a billboard or a bulletin board?

a poem or a story?

an alarm clock or a wake-up call?

a dam or a waterfall?

a microscope or a telescope?

Texas or Wisconsin?

hardware or software?

a Post-it Note© or a voicemail?

a book or television?

a motor cross or a street racer?

the puzzle or the solution?

private or public?

an electric shaver or a razor?

a cave or a tree house?

radio or television?

a movie or a play?

order or confusion?

a farm or a ranch?

panicked or relaxed?

expected or surprised?

a chair or a couch?

happy or sad?

a bowl or a plate?

fish or steak?

a rocking chair or a wing back?

Ansel Adams or Leroy Neiman?

a No Trespassing sign or a Welcome mat?

a morning run or an afternoon stroll?

a climber or a digger?

an ant or a grasshopper?

recycle it or toss it?

flowering or hibernating?

an assistant or a rival?

an antonym or a synonym?

a full scale or a model?

expensive or free?

a dress shirt or a T-shirt?

a castle or a fortress?

work, rest, or play?

fair or foul?

body guard or a life guard?

the rose or the thorns?

an architect or a demolition man?

a donation or a grant?

a book or a book end?

a peacemaker or a troublemaker?

fussion or fission?

a sailor or a soldier?

a brown bag or a school lunch?

a one-way street or a two-way street?

a hearing aid or eyeglasses?

rain or shine?

a girl or a woman?

the chip or the dip?

a Greek tragedy or a science fiction novel?

pancakes or waffles?

credit or debit?

fire or ice?

a pillow or a rock?

a fireplace or a fountain?

city lights or stars?

an allusion or a specification?

a Butler or a Chauffeur?

a freeze or a thaw?

a clap or a whistle?

a backpack or a briefcase?

deliberate or spontaneous?

a talk show or a news report?

cooked or raw?

a bag or a box?

"Share the wealth" or "To each his/her own"?

a silouhette or a portrait?

a paper towel or a washcloth?

a bagel or a donut?

paper towels or a Kleenex©?

curly or straight?

the circus or the zoo?

custom made or factory direct?

the alarm or the snooze button?

fast or slow?

a brick or a stone?

snow skiing or water skiing?

a balcony or a porch?

early or late?

Broadway or Hollywood?

a perfectionist or easygoing?

leather or lace?

a spaceship or a submarine?

a camper or a tent?

overnight or standard ground?

astroturf or grass?

over the counter or prescription?

lotion or oil?

country pine or new car smell?

an artist or a patron?

pig out or work out?

a custom or a fad?

the fox or the hound?

a rainbow or a thunderstorm?

a frame or a picture?

the continuous line or dotted line on the

an advantage or a handicap?

a canoe or a jet ski?

a gradual grade or steep grade?

a conventional oven or a microwave?

a beach towel or a lounge chair?

plastic utensils or sterling silverware?

against the wind or with the wind?

a dash or a cup?

a bed or a sleeping bag?

the sunrise or the sunset?

gum or licorice?

a playhouse or a tree house?

baked or fried?

a ballad or rock 'n' roll?

a road or a straightaway?

ice cream or frozen yogurt?

in fashion or out of style?

a twist or a shout?

a foot or a hand?

Canada or Mexico?

a tank top or a T-shirt?

a billboard or a bumper sticker?

excellent or imperfect?

a camp or a country club?

lost or found?

long hair or short hair?

Thanksgiving or Valentine's day?

a cattle car or cattle drive?

pictures or slides?

natural or florescent lighting?

a lecture or a party?

the problem or the solution?

dental floss or a toothpick?

adventurous or cautious?

AM or FM radio?

rain or snow?

a deposit or a withdrawal?

going or staying?

a saver or a spender?

a goose or a turkey?

criticism or flattery?

a week or a lifetime?

a chair or a table?

the high wire or the trapeze?

practical or theoretical?

a cruise ship or a yacht?

blocks or Legos©?

a reader or a writer?

an answer or a question?

a dishwasher or a hand washer?

blue or pink?

Winter, Spring, Summer, or Fall?

horizontal or vertical?

the next right or the next stop?

the beginning or the end?

a junkyard or a rose garden?

a dunk shot or a jump shot?

a bag clip or a twist tie?

an ice sculpture or a sand castle?

detergent or bleach?

"Full steam ahead" or "Take the long way home"?

casual or formal?

abstract or concrete?

bones or muscles?

feminine or masculine?

a caterpillar or a butterfly?

a dreamer or a realist?

the funny papers or the front page?

minor details or a general overview?

Peter Pan® or Wendy®?

a comic book or a history book?

a noun or a verb?

a tropical breeze or crisp mountain air?

awake or sleepy?

Saturday or Sunday?

downhill or uphill?

Hide-and-seek or "Lost and found"?

smart or stupid?

the high jump or the long jump?

diamonds or hearts?

back-to-back or face-to-face?

a clamp or a paper weight?

"In the cards" or "A sure thing"?

directory assistance (information) or the phone book?

a shoe box or a shoe rack?

self service or a waiter?

a backpack or a duffle bag?

the drum or the stick?

box seats or general admission?

a sun lover or a star gazer?

the judge or the jury?

a shield or a spear?

a blueberry or a raspberry?

line dry or tumble dry?

exactly or just about right?

abrupt or polite?

an only child or a sibling?

perishable or durable?

a hang glider or a parachute?

cheese or pepperoni pizza?

a buffet or menu item?

a bridge or a tunnel?

the force or the fulcrum?

the chicken or the egg?

going around or going through?

Outward Bound© or an urban adventure?

serious or funny?

a coloring book or a sketch book?

salted or unsalted?

electrical or manual?

a full room or an empty room?

active or idle?

an exercise bike or a treadmill?

bar soap or liquid soap?

stain remover or tiedye?

a steak or a salad?

ice or water?

a stalactite or a stalagmite?

sun screen or sun block?

a drawbridge or a moat?

the horse or the wagon?

a contract or a handshake?

left or right?

food or drinks?

a buyer or a trader?

stretching or weightlifting?

a beanbag chair or a Lazyboy©?

et cetera or period?

a bicycle or a tricycle?

common sense or a day dreamer?

the lightning or the thunder?

inseparable or divisible?

a life boat or a life jacket?

a miser or a philanthropist?

fact or fiction?

a bell or a buzzer?

a snake or a spider?

neccesary or optional?

right-side-up or up-side-down?

a roller coaster or a merry-go-round?

shingles or tiles?

sunny side up or sunny side over?

a tackle box or a tool box?

a hill or a valley?

a dog or a puppy?

forgiving or remembering?

a freckle or a dimple?

a bungee jump or a sky dive?

a mail box or a mail person?

play-by-play or uninterupted?

live or taped?

a wedding or a funeral?

furnished or unfurnished?

a talker or a thinker?

Mother Teresa or the Dalai Lama?

a nurse or a patient?

a note or a rest?

get over it or get with it?

vanilla ice cream or orange sherbert?

a camillian or a gacko?

a chandelier or a candle?

a sparkler or a firecracker?

a puller or a pusher?

a guide dog or a guide book?

a referee or a player?

a refuge or a refugee?

yes or no?

Aspen, Colorado or Orlando, Florida?

a ditto or a question mark?

face-to-face or side-by-side?

paper or plastic?

the heart or the brain?

the jitter bug or the waltz?

........add your own!

Are You More Like......

About The Authors

SUSANA ACOSTA, M.A., has been a Spanish and English teacher for over twenty years. She was recognized by her school as a Master Teacher and can be found in the 2002 edition of "Who's Who in American Teachers." Susana was born in Madrid, Spain and stayed in school there until she received her Masters Degree in Art History from the University of Madrid. She taught hundreds of children how to speak Spanish and English, managed several businesses, climbed mountains and traveled extensively. This is Susana's first publication but assuredly not her last.

CHRIS CAVERT, M.S., has been active with groups of all ages for over 22 years. He is known around the United States as a trainer and speaker in the area of Adventure Based Activity Programming and focuses on how activities within this field help to develop and enhance pro-social behaviors,especially with youth populations. Chris holds a Physical Education Teaching Degree from the University of Wisconsin-La Crosse and a Masters Degree in Experiential Education from Minnesota State University at Mankato, specializing in curriculum development.

Some of his first writing was published in the best selling Chicken Soup for the Soul series by Jack Canfield and Mark Victor Hansen. His activities have been published in books by Karl Rohnke, Sam Sikes, and Jim Cain. Since then Chris has written six books and co-authored three others. They include:

E.A.G.E.R. Curriculum
Affordable Portables

Games (and other stuff) for Group, Books 1& 2
Richochet and Other Fun Games With an Odd Ball
Games (and other stuff) for Teachers, with Laurie Frank
50 Ways to Use Your Noodle: Loads of Land Games with
Foam Noodle Toys, with Sam Sikes
50 More Ways to Use Your Noodle: Loads of Land
Games with Foam Noodle Toys, with Sam Sikes
What Would it Be Like: 1001 Anytime Questions for
Anysize Answers

Chris' books focus on sharing activities that help educa-
tors in many different fields use experiential/adventure
education to encourage pro-social behaviors in groups
they work with. For more information about Chris'
publications and training opportunities, visit his site at:
www.fundoing.com. To purchase any of his books, call
Wood 'N' Barnes Publishing at 1-800-678-0621.